EDWARD LEAR IN GREECE

COVER: KHANEA (CATALOGUE NO. 70)

EDWARD LEAR IN GREECE

A LOAN EXHIBITION FROM THE GENNADIUS LIBRARY, ATHENS

CIRCULATED BY

THE INTERNATIONAL EXHIBITIONS FOUNDATION

1971-1972

PARTICIPATING MUSEUMS

Amherst College
Amherst, Massachusetts

California Palace of the Legion of Honor
San Francisco, California

The Walters Art Gallery
Baltimore, Maryland

The Columbus Gallery of Fine Arts
Columbus, Ohio

The Art Institute of Chicago
Chicago, Illinois

Museum of Fine Arts
Houston, Texas

The University of Georgia
Athens, Georgia

Columbia Museum of Art
Columbia, S. C.

TRUSTEES OF THE INTERNATIONAL EXHIBITIONS FOUNDATION

COPYRIGHT © 1971 BY INTERNATIONAL EXHIBITIONS FOUNDATION

LIBRARY OF CONGRESS CATALOGUE CARD NUMBER 72–154602

TYPESET AT THE STINEHOUR PRESS PRINTED BY THE MERIDEN GRAVURE COMPANY

FOREWORD

FOR ALL its troubled history, Greece—'Fair Greece, sad relic'—has been fortunate in the artists who visited it and recorded for posterity its monuments, its landscape, and its people. The list is long and honorable, beginning with Cyriacus of Ancona in 1435 and continuing until the advent of photography largely usurped the role of the artist. Edward Lear (1812–1888) is one of the last in this series of notable artist-travellers, but it is he who above all wins our affection. He loved Greece and knew it well, and in his sketches captures the outlines and depth of its dramatic and varied landscape more successfully perhaps than any artist before or since.

Among its treasure the Gennadius Library numbers over two hundred of Lear's drawings, dating from 1848 to 1866, mostly of Greece, a few of adjacent areas. Large as the collection is, it represents no more than a fraction, perhaps less than a quarter, of his total Greek output. For he was an industrious and prolific worker. During a five-week tour of Crete, in 1864, he made at least 179 drawings, of which we have 92, seven of them done in a single day. The date and the hour of each are meticulously noted: 24 April, 5 A.M., 8 A.M., 9 A.M., 9:30 A.M., 11:30 A.M., 1 P.M., 6 P.M. His general practice, especially when travelling, was to sketch rapidly in pencil, adding various notations to remind him of details and colors. Later, at leisure, the drawings (notes and all) were 'penned out' and finally some color was usually added. For the sketches were never intended for the public. They were personal memoranda, models for an eventual lithograph or, when commissioned, for an oil painting. Today, they are generally esteemed, for their spontaneity and freshness, far more than his finished paintings. And the gentle humor of the notations often reminds us that the artist was also the author of the *Book of Nonsense*.

Under his will the drawings passed *en masse* to his friend Franklin Lushington and it was not until forty years later, when the collection was sold to a London dealer, that the real talent of the half-forgotten Victorian artist began to win recognition. Early in 1929 the dealer, Craddock & Barnard, offered a number of fine Greek ones to Joannes Gennadius, the retired Greek Minister at the Court of St. James's.

Mr. Gennadius felt unable to pay for them himself but persuaded the American School of Classical Studies at Athens, to which in 1922 he had presented his magnificent collection of books on Greece, to purchase the lot. They agreed, not without some hesitation, and thus acquired 192 drawings—for the sum total of £25, about 65 cents apiece! It was a sound investment. Ten years later the library was able to add thirteen others, mostly uncolored, but at a considerably higher price.

For many years a selection of the Lears has been one of the favorite exhibits for visitors to the Gennadius Library. We are grateful to the International Exhibitions Foundation for making it possible now to share our delight in them with a larger public. Our warm thanks are due also to Mr. Philip Hofer, Lear's foremost advocate and connoisseur, for writing the Introduction; to Miss Eleanor Garvey of the Houghton Library for many kind services; to Professor Spyridon Marinatos, Inspector General of Antiquities, and to the Archaeological Service for permission to send the drawings abroad for restoration and exhibition; and to Mr. Frank Doloff for undertaking the delicate task of restoring the drawings to their original freshness.

FRANCIS R. WALTON
Director, Gennadius Library

INTRODUCTION

FEW art lovers, outside of visitors to the American School of Classical Studies' Gennadius Library in Athens, are aware that this lovely building houses the most comprehensive selection of Edward Lear's Greek watercolors to be seen at any institution in the world, although Dr. Francis Walton, the Director, is always generously ready to show them. It is usually assumed that the Houghton Library, Harvard University, must be paramount, since it has more Lear drawings by far than any other European or American collection. But the simple fact is that while Mr. W. B. O. Field, and the writer of this foreword, were buying Harvard's over four thousand Lear sketches of all kinds, Mr. Joannes Gennadius was quietly assembling subjects representing his native land in the London market at an average price of about five shillings each! In the end, he was able to secure the acquisition of over two hundred which entered the Library that now bears his name. Seventy of the very best of these are represented in this catalogue, of which only eight have been shown in America before (at the Worcester, Massachusetts, Art Museum in the late spring of 1968). They have all been cleaned and re-matted by Mr. Frank Doloff of the Boston Museum of Fine Arts—a very necessary operation occasioned by the use, in Lear's day, of paper-board 'mats' containing wood pulp which discolors with age, staining the drawings themselves. Now all the drawings in this exhibition seem 'safe' for the foreseeable future, a precaution Dr. Walton insisted upon, and all other Lear collectors should take, unless their drawings have been recently (and expertly) inspected, and cleaned.

This exhibition is exceedingly important not only because Greece was Lear's favorite country, but also because there are no landscape watercolors of Greece from Classical or Mediaeval times, and few indeed from more recent periods. Lear's drawings are the best artistic interpretations that exist before modern construction, tourism, and industrialization visibly intruded, spoiling the calm nostalgic beauty of the Greek mainland, and the islands, both in the Aegean and Ionian Seas.

On Lear's first trip to Greece in 1848, when he was thirty-six years old and a well trained topographical draughtsman, he visited Corfù—then Attica and other parts of the southern portion of the peninsula—later Constantinople, and back by boat to Salonika, in the northern reaches of Greece, as it is now constituted. Then he immediately undertook a long, arduous horseback journey in order to visit Macedonia, Albania, and Epirus. Many of the finest and largest Gennadius drawings come from this expedition and from his trip to Crete in 1864, as do the best of the Harvard ones as well. Lear made a number of later trips in 1849, 1855–58, and he lived on the island of Corfù from 1861 to 1864. He also visited Mt. Athos several times. So it can be seen that he covered Greece very effectively, as even few modern travellers have done. But after that he returned only for fleeting visits. His last stay was at Corfù in 1877. At sixty-five, he was a tired old man, who hardly moved from San Remo on the Italian Riviera except for summer holidays in Northern Italy and Switzerland.

After this travelling exhibition, for which the Officers and Trustees of the American School of Classical Studies are deeply indebted to the International Exhibitions Foundation, the Gennadius drawings will return to Athens, where they may eventually be housed in the new wing of the 'Morgan Library' of Eastern Europe for which the School is currently raising funds.

PHILIP HOFER
Cambridge, Massachusetts

CATALOGUE

1. ZANTE
APRIL 27, 1848
'Foreground, Cistus, squills, aloes, reed canes, yellow & pink flowers.' (18)

2. VOSTIZZA
MARCH 9, 1849

3. MEGASPELION
MARCH 10, 1849

4. NEAR KALAVRYTA
MARCH 11, 1849

5. LAKE OF PHONIA
MARCH 13, 1849, 9:00 A.M.
'Vast gray rox.' 'No pine at all.' 'A immensely thick pinewood. Stems & branches endless—light off.' (15)

6. MANTINEA
MARCH 15, 1849
'You may make the plain larger, and the line of wall XXX lower if you like—not much though.' 'ABCDE Progressively distant fields, with heaps of ruin here & there.' (25)

7. KARYTENA
MARCH 16, 1849, 10:00 A.M.
'The original of this drawing is one of 6 given to F[ranklyn] L[ushington] traced and penned out for me by F. Underhill July 1866.' 'Ye blacke dwarfe, 3 feet high.' (34)

8. ON MT. ITHOME
MARCH 21, 1849, 10:30 A.M.
'Early morning—tone all gray.' 'Lilac & green—infinite.' 'Tops of tame olives.' 'Wild olives—gray rox.' (55)

9. BELOW TAYGETUS (KALYBEA)
MARCH 22, 1849, 6:15 P.M.
'Tone, after sunset, awful dark (& the sun fell, & all the land was dark).' (63)

10. SPARTA
MARCH 23, 1849, 2:30–3:00 P.M.
'Mountain—glasslike snow—with dark patches of minute pines.' (65)

11. MYCENAE
MARCH 31, 1849, 7:00 A.M.
'Chasms of gray rocks, perpendicular, spotted here & there with shrubs, and dashed with red ochre, Amalfioise.' 'Walls very red & oker.' 'Gray rox.' 'Time & Assfiddle [Thyme & asphodel].' 'Abis [abyss].' (96)

12. CORINTH
APRIL 1, 1849, 11:30 A.M.
'Camel Bey—his house.' 'A depth full of sheep, goats & other vegebles.' 'Gotes.' (109)

13. NEAR KINETA
APRIL 2, 1849
'Immense quantity of heaps of ded branches with dry red leaves.' 'The brighest yellow green in the world can never equal these pines.' (112)

14. KAKI-SCALA
APRIL 2, 1849, 2:00 P.M.
'Lentisk stalks gray—ditto olives, & pines.' (114)

15. MEGARA
APRIL 2, 1849, 4:30 P.M.
'Olives all old & lean.' 'All nasty orrid bare hills.' (116)

16. COLONIUS (CAPE COLONA)
APRIL 6, 1849

17. ATHENS
APRIL 8, 1849, 3:00 P.M.
'Windy!!' 'lights on Acropolis, red, ochre, all.' [Note 'totality' and line of horison.] (136)

18. ATHENS
APRIL 8, 1849, 3:30–4:30 P.M.
'Shepherd' 'Sheep.' (137)

19. ATHENS
APRIL 8, 1849, 5:00 P.M.

20. ATHENS
APRIL 8–9, 1949, 7:00 P.M. & 6:00 A.M.
'Flowers [asphodel] pale pink, many lower leaves dry—dead—red oker.—flower stalks, brown red madder.' (142)

21. ATHENS FROM KARÁ
APRIL 9, 1849, 5:00 P.M.
'Ravines, & sunset. Misty gloom.' (143B)

22. PLATAEA
APRIL 11, 1849, 4:00 P.M.
'10,000,000 goats.' (155)

23. PARNASSUS
APRIL 12, 1849, 2:00 P.M.
'Young sycamore—Euphorbia—fig—arum—Very vegetable bank.—Tiber banks, dark, shade all.—domestic bramble—fennel—asphodels—Yell. euphorbia in heaps.—Anemone.' 'Tortoises!!!' 'Incredible plains—blu lake—marshy lake.' (162)

24. PARNASSUS (& LIVADHIA)
APRIL 12, 1849, 5:30 P.M.
'Greeny gray & black & yellow brown lichen.' 'Tones—X very dark. XX darkest of all. 2. next in depth—& all above infinitely misty & pale.' (164)

25. CHAERONEA
APRIL 13, 1849

26. DELPHI
APRIL 16, 1849, 6:45 P.M.
'Let the light catch the houses.' (191)

27. SALONA
APRIL 17, 1849

28. SALONA
APRIL 17, 1849

29. SALONA [AMPHISSA]
APRIL 17–18, 1849, 6:30 P.M.–6:30 A.M.
'Castle & rock very red—B. Sienna & ochre.' (199)

30. CHOREPISKOPOS
JUNE 12–14, 1856

31. NIPHES
JUNE 22, 1856

32. NIPHES
JUNE 23, 1856

33. NIPHES
JUNE 21, 1856, 7:00 P.M.
'Penned out March 20, 1863.' (34)

34. SALONIKI
SEPT. 23, 1856

35. CAVALLA
SEPT. 26, 1856
'The lines to the right of the castle are, I think a mistake, not rubbed off.' [In distance: Thasos (left), Mt. Athos (right).] (—)

36. TROY
SEPT. 30, 1856

37. BOUTRINTO
MARCH 7, 1857

38. JOANNINA
APRIL 10, 1857
'Lilac gray green.' (—)

39. BAIA [EPIRUS]
APRIL 14, 1857, 8:00 A.M.
'Speckled & spotted with various colours and unmarkable tints.' (—)

40. KONITZA
APRIL 16, 1857

41. PALAIOKASTRITZA [CORFU]
APRIL 16–17–18–19–20, 1862
'New cypresses not dark—gold-sided.' 'Rox, very bright white gray.' (9)

42. BELOW BOUNIATADES [CORFU]
MAY 5, 1862
'Olives, dark below—hoary above.' 'Hill—gray lilac green.' 'Fields & sheep bright through olives.' (56)

43. GOVINO ROAD [CORFU]
FEB. 24, 1863, 4:30 P.M.
'Trees very dark brown off sky.' (—)

44. CORFU [MT. SAN SALVADOR]
APRIL 2, 1863

45. ITHACA
APRIL 28, 1863

46. APTERA
MAY 3, 1864

47. APTERA [CRETE]
MAY 4, 1864, 7:00 A.M.
'Salvia—squills—prinari—cistus—euphorbia.' 'O O—light on the sea.' (69)

48. FROM APTERA
MAY 4, 1864, 5:30 A.M.
'Gray stones, green & gray herbidges.' 'But the best effect was on the preevious evening.' (73)

49. FROM EXOPOLIS
MAY 5, 1864, 5:30 A.M.
'1. Ida pale. 2. less. 20. much nearer & deeper. 40. green begins.' (74)

50. EXOPOLI
MAY 5, 1864, 6:00 A.M.
'Whole scene dark except sea & sky & Ida line of mountains.' (75)

51. LIMNI KOURNA
MAY 5, 1864, 9:00 A.M.
'All gritty gray green.' 'Echo of green.' (77)

52. RETHYMNOS
MAY 7, 1864, 8:00 A.M.
'Corn—red earth—banx.' (91)

53. RETHYMNOS
MAY 7, 1864, 6:30 P.M.
'White chalky road.' (90)

54. MEGALOKASTRON [HERAKLION]
MAY 10–12, 1864, 4:00 P.M.–7:00 A.M.
'Flox of goats and fat tailed sheep.' (117)

55. MOUNT JUKTAS
MAY 14, 1864, 8:00 A.M.
'Green & red leaves, some burnt.' 'Asphodels, one in bloom.'
'Perpendicular dark brown red gray rox.' (127)

56. AGHIOS THOMAS
MAY 15, 1864

57. AGHIOS THOMAS
MAY 15, 1864, 5:10 P.M.
'These are warblers *potamidhes* [in Greek] which sing all the time
and live all year with us in our country.' (140)

58. GORTYNA
MAY 17, 1864, 5:00 A.M.
'See Campagna ruins, but grayer.' 'Masses of the ruined Theatre
—gray stones & bits of red tile—Ruined gray & brown walls
everywhere.' 'Earwigs!' (144)

59. GORTYNA
MAY 17, 1864, 7–8:00 A.M.
'Hills choc. gray okery.' 'Thissels.' (146)

60. BOBBE
MAY 18, 1864

61. KAKOVOUNO
MAY 21, 1864

62. PETRAS KANARAS
MAY 21, 1864, 7:30 A.M.

63. APOKORONAS
MAY 21, 1864, 8:00 A.M.

64. APOKORONAS
MAY 22, 1864, 6:30 A.M.

65. SUDA BAY
MAY 24, 1864, 5:00 A.M.
'Athos pale—the Melipotamos hill *very* pale.' 'Immensely bright,
clearly pure.' (160)

66. APOKORONA
MAY 24, 1864
.

67. APOKORONA
MAY 24, 1864, 9:30 A.M.
'Bright oxide chro green corn.' 'Corn flat.' (163)

68. PSILORITIS FROM PHRÉ
MAY 25, 1864

69. KHANEA
MAY 27, 1864, 5–6:00 P.M.
'Hills purply gray russet greeny.' 'Green cum mallows.' (175)

70. KHANEA

MAY 28, 1864, 5:30–6:00 P.M.

'Catch gold light grass & asphodel.' 'All the distance is very pale blue-gray fern [?] not dark nor red.' 'City pale—rest beyond paler, farthest promontories not clear.' 'Stems of olives, Indigo, Ind Red, & oker, *very* dark.' (176)

71. CORFU

APRIL 21, 1866, 9–10:00 A.M.

'Work out all distance in blue.' (25)

72. LAKE OF SKODRA FROM TZERNAGOVA

APRIL 30, 1866, 1–1:30 P.M.

'Distance very lovely faint.' 'Work out all the distances in blues.' (26)

73. SPALATO

MAY 8, 1866

I. ZANTE

2. VOSTIZZA

3. MEGASPELION

4. NEAR KALAVRYTA

5. LAKE OF PHONIA

6. MANTINEA

7. KARYTENA

8. ON MT. ITHOME

9. BELOW TAYGETUS (KALYBEA)

10. SPARTA

II. MYCENAE

Corinth.
April 1. (11½ A.M.)
1849

Camel Bey - his horse.

gray stone pale

a depth field of sheep,
goats & other vegetables.

12. CORINTH

13. NEAR KINETA

14. KAKI-SCALA

15. MEGARA

16. COLONIUS (CAPE COLONA)

Athens.
8. April. 1849.
3. P.M.   (cloudy!!)

Lights on Acropolis,
         red, ochre, etc.

lights on Acropolis
         red ochre etc.

(136)

17. ATHENS

Athens.
8. April 1849.
3½ P.M.

Sandy.

Shepherd

Sheep

(137)

18. ATHENS

19. ATHENS

Athens.
8 & 9. April. 1849
6 AM.   7 PM.

flowers pale pink
many lower leaves dry — dead — red chor.
flower stalks, brown. red mud

(142)

20. ATHENS

21. ATHENS FROM KARÁ

22. PLATAEA

23. PARNASSUS

24. PARNASSUS (& LIVADHIA)

Cheronea. April. 13.1849.
16¾ A.M.

Cheronea
10¾. April 13. 1849

25. CHAERONEA

Delphi.
6/4. April 16. 1849.

let the light catch the houses

191

26. DELPHI

near Salona.
April 17. 1844 (4.P.M.)

27. SALONA

Salona.
6.P.M. April 17, 1849.

198

28. SALONA

29. SALONA [AMPHISSA]

30. CHOREPISKOPOS

31. NIPHES

32. NIPHES

33. NIPHES

34. SALONIKI

35. CAVALLA

Troy.
30. Sept. 1856.

36. TROY

37. BOUTRINTO

38. JOANNINA

39. BAIA (EPIRUS)

40. KONITZA

56

41. PALAIOKASTRITZA [CORFU]

42. BELOW BOUNIATADES [CORFU]

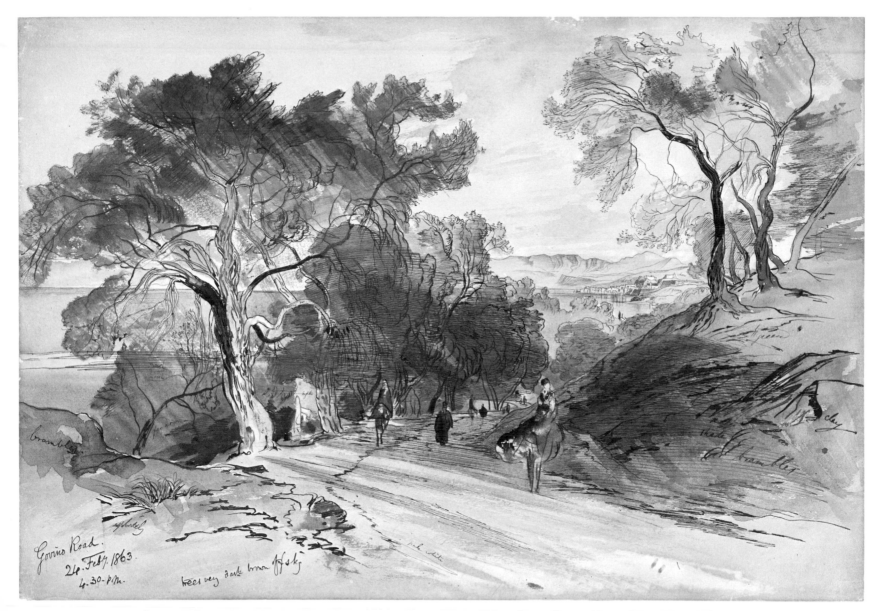

Govino Road.
24 Feb 1863.
4.30 P.M.

trees very dark brown off sky

43. GOVINO ROAD [CORFU]

44. CORFU [MT. SAN SALVADOR]

45. ITHACA

46. APTERA

Salvia
& Squills

Aptera.   4 May
J.dell.   1864.   (69)

47. APTERA [CRETE]

48. FROM APTERA

49. FROM EXOPOLIS

50. EXOPOLI

66

51. LIMNI KOURNA

52. RETHYMNOS

53. RETHYMNOS

54. MEGALOKASTRON [HERAKLION]

55. MOUNT JUKTAS

56. AGHIOS THOMAS

57. AGHIOS THOMAS

58. GORTYNA

59. GORTYNA

60. BOBBE

61. KAKOVOUNO

62. PETRAS KANARAS

63. APOKORONAS

64. APOKORONAS

65. SUDA BAY

66. APOKORONA

67. APOKORONA

68. PSILORITIS FROM PHRÉ

69. KHANEA

70. KHANEA

84

71. CORFU

72. LAKE OF SKODRA FROM TZERNAGOVA

6. PM. May 8. 1866. Spálato

73. SPALATO